To my love,
& roommate forever,

Hannah

—Hell

June 2015
When we were young,
carefree, and full of life.

The author wishes to thank Woman magazine for
permission to use those cartoons from this selection
which originally appeared in Woman

To Dotty, a Calico Cat

**A continuation of CAT-alogue
(first published 1976)
and Magnifi-CAT
(first published 1977)**

Published by William Collins Sons and Co Ltd
First published 1978
Copyright © Woman magazine 1978
Printed in Great Britain

ISBN 0 00 410334 3

TRIPLI~CAT

Bruce Angrave

Collins Glasgow and London

Chau-fur

Fur-st Footer

Pussion Flower

Tom-ahawk

S-fur-inx

Ar-kit-ect

Jum-purr

Anti Purr-s-purr-ant

Mew-la-la

Purr-icey

E-paw-lettes

Pro-purr-ganda

Dispro-paw-tionate

Purr-destrian
Under-puss

Purr-esident Carter

Le-purr-echaun

Caco-fur-ny

Claw-roform

Sher-purr

Slip-purr-y

Mos-kit-o

Oom-purr-purr

Hair S-purr-ay

Fur-ench

Acro-paw-lis

Pom-puss

Statue of Li-purr-ty

Purr-ilous

Phos-fur-escent

Whim-purr

S-purr-ned

Cam-purr

La-paw-atory
Ex-purr-iment

Purr-lican

Puss-tle & Mortar

Paw-ridge

Puss-enger

Purr de deux

Kit-e

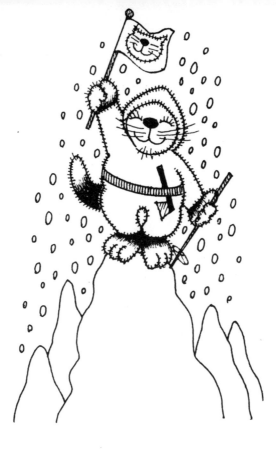

Mt. E-fur-est

Fur-saken

Puss-ers-by

South Purr-cific

Rum-puss

Ne-fur-titi

Wallpa-purr

Paw-n

Puss-h chair

St. Paw-l's

Paw-ter

Frank-fur-ters

Puss-tachio

Pan-tom-ime

Fur-tree

Purr-spex

Bas-kit

Snow Fur-lakes

Ex-purr-esso

Strip-purr

Un-fur-led

Bruce Angrave has worked in advertising agencies, written and illustrated children's books, drawn for Punch, contributed verse to the New Yorker and designed posters for London Transport. He has given many talks on the radio and received the British Academy Award for his first venture in television design. He is a specialist in paper-sculpture, much of which has been shown in public expositions including Expo 70 Japan. He has drawn for Woman almost as long as he can remember.
For recreation he collects enormous automatic music machines.

Tail piece